ISBN 0 85079 186.3

RUPERT FUN

Express Books

Published by Express Newspapers plc, 245 Blackfriars Road, London, SE1 9UX
Printed by Purnell Book Production Ltd., Paulton, Bristol, England.

U.K. £1.99

CONTENTS

© 1989 Express Newspapers plc, 245 Blackfriars Road, London, SE1 9UX

Stories as adapted by OBERON BV, Holland, from the original works of the late Alfred Bestall, M.B.E., with translations by Marinet Parker and editing by James Henderson. Cover and new illustrations by Francis Phillipps.

RUPERT

and

DOG TOBY

A visit to Punch and Judy land is something new for Rupert but it really did happen during his summer holiday.

The weather is lovely. Rupert is on holiday at home and he is really enjoying his book...

This book is so exciting, Daddy!

That's nice.

A letter has just come from Bruno!

My brother wants you to come and stay, Rupert.

Oh, great! He lives by the sea!

That's your swimming trunks bought.

Oh, look Mummy!

May I have a pail and spade?

Remember, do behave And none of your wild adventures!

Next day Rupert's father takes him to the station where he meets a new friend...

Hello, I'm Toby. I'm off to Sandy Bay. Where are you going?

I'm Rupert. And I'm going there too!

Come and visit me there!

I'm a sort of actor You'll find me on the beach.

Oh, Daddy, may I ride in the guard's van too? It'll be nice to keep Toby company!

Good idea!

I'll go and ask!

Of course he may, sir. I'll keep an eye on them!

It'll be much nicer having you along!

Where do you do your acting, Toby?

In a Punch and Judy show on the beach.

We've arrived! Put your cases on the platform.

Thanks, guard!

Hooray! Sandy Bay!

Then Rupert has an idea. He'll play a joke on Uncle Bruno...

Here comes Uncle Bruno. Quick, Toby, hide!

This'll be a good laugh!

Now watch this!

I don't understand. He was here a minute ago. There's his case!

This is Uncle Bruno's car. Come on, let's get in!

Are you sure I may come?

Of course! But don't show yourself 'til we're moving!

As the car moves off Rupert and Toby pop up. But the joke is on them!

PEEKABOO! Hello, Uncle!

Oh, no! This isn't your Uncle's car!

LITTLE RASCALS! Go and play your tricks on someone else!

Let's get out of here!

Sorry, mister!

Oo! Ice cream! My treat, Rupert.

Did you notice the monkey?

Poor little thing! He looks starved. Let's help him escape!

Off you go! Quickly!

HEY! WHAT'S ALL THIS? What are you playing at?

5

Just you pair wait 'til I get my hands on you!

Serve you right, rotten cruel thing!

That was a daring thing to do!

Bruno Bear! Is this your uncle's house?

Yes. But I don't think he's back yet. Wait! I hear a car!

HA HA! Surprise, surprise, Uncle!

Rupert! All right, I know it was a joke. But I was worried!

Uncle Bruno takes the joke in good part but Rupert has to promise there'll be no more...

Your new boss was at the station, Toby. He looked surprised you weren't there.

Oh, gosh! I'll have to tell him that...OOPS!

What shall I do? I don't have his address. He was meeting me off the train!

Luckily for you I think I know where his Punch and Judy show is.

And so. Half an hour later...

Pablo's show? It's over there, mister!

Thank you very much!

Hello, Mr. Pablo! Just see who I have here!

There you are Toby! Glad you've made it!

Toby is introduced to the other players and the show soon gets under way.

BRAVO! BRAVO!

Hey, Rupert. That wasn't bad, was it! See you later, right?

Later that day Rupert and Uncle Bruno are enjoying the sun and sand when...

"Hey...pssst! Rupert Bear!"

"A note from Toby. See you tonight!"

"See me tonight? Why?"

"Rupert, I told the other actors about you. They want to meet you. Pick you up at midnight. We'll have fun, Toby."

And then...

"Hey, Rupert. Wake up!"

"Rupert, meet Punch, Judy the clown and the constable. Come on out!"

"We have to work during the day, so we must have our fun now."

"All clear! Come on!"

And so a very odd group head for the empty beach...

"Toby, what have you got planned?"

"Just enjoying the beach and the sea. Remember we can't during the day."

"We've got lots of nice things to eat!"

"This is fun!"

"A midnight picnic!"

The picnic's such fun the night passes quickly.

Look! It's getting light...

The tide's coming in!

We really should go!

Hang on! The clown has disappeared!

CLOWN! WHERE ARE YOU?

His hat! It was in the water!

He surely can't have...

No! Look! There he is.

He's fallen asleep.

Rupert, what shall we do? He can't swim!

Don't worry I'll look after this!

Oh, well done, Rupert!

Rupert, I can't thank you enough!

We must do something about Rupert. He's soaked!

Punch says that's been empty for ages. You can get dry in there.

There is some hay in the shed and Toby has an idea...

 We'll make a fire and dry your things!

 ♪♪ Here we go round... ♪♪
♪ ...the clothes dryer... ♪

 What's going on out there?

 It's that ice cream man!
Quick, everyone! Run!

 But the man catches Toby. Things look bad...

 Well, then...
I've got a bone to pick with you!

 He's got Toby. Now what?
In the name of the law, let him go!

 He's taking no notice. We must think of something else

 Uncle Bruno must be told. That's all there is about it...

 What's he going to say about a midnight picnic!

 More bother, and you're only just here!
I know! I'm sorry! But what can we do?

9

Uncle Bruno thinks Rupert should go and see if perhaps Toby has been set free...

Hello, little bear. It's lovely to be free! Thanks!

Look, you've got to help me now!

Your boss has taken my friend Toby prisoner. What can we do?

If he treats him like me he'll have a bad time!

There they are! Toby's taken your place!

I suppose we'd best follow them...

Wait! Look! A car! It's stopped!

Well, well! Another of your tricks, eh?

Look, I'm sorry about yesterday. It was a mistake, truly!

Luckily he's a good sport and ready to help...

I was young once myself. I've an idea...

There he is! Fingers crossed, everyone!

Now, you look happy when customers appear...or else!

HEY! MY HAT!

What's going on?

The monkey scampers off with the hat. The man chases it. Now's Rupert's chance...

COME BACK!

Come on now! Quick, Toby!

QUICKLY! Mr. Pig's helping us!

GREAT! It's worked!

Well done! Into the car quickly!

Cool down, nasty! Have one of your own ice creams!

RASCALS! VILLAINS! Oh, I'll get you yet!

Mr. Pig drops the friends off at the pier where Uncle Bruno is waiting...

Uncle Bruno! Everything's all right!

That afternoon...

We hope that you've enjoyed our show now...

...I ask my very good friend Rupert Bear to step forward!

It's thanks to Rupert that we can be here to perform for you!

Hooray!

Good old Rupert!

I was jolly nervous in front of all those people!

Oh, you get over it! In fact, I think you'd make a good actor!

But Rupert has too many adventures in store for him to think of that...

SEASIDE PUZZLE

    Rupert and his pals are on holiday at the seaside. On their way to the beach they pass a shrimp stall, and this gives the little bear an idea. "Let's take a look round and see how many things we can find that start with the letter S," he says. Bill and Podgy agree, and so they have a competition. Rupert won by getting 32—can you beat him? (Turn to the back of the cover for Rupert's list.)

RUPERT'S CLOCK PUZZLE

    Rupert and Bill are being shown over Farmer Wurzle's buildings. "What a whopping big clock!" cries the little bear. "Ar, 'tis the biggest farm clock in the country," says Mr. Wurzle. "It had an accident when it was put up. The face got broken into four pieces and when we picked them up we found that the figures when added individually (*i.e. X* as ten, *V* as five and *I* as one, all instances) on each piece added up to the same amount. The broken edges all met at the centre. Can you tell where the breaks must have come?"

    (Well, can you?)

RUPERT'S BALLOON PUZZLE

"There's the balloon man," says Rupert, "and, look, the wind has blown his balloons into a circle. I wish I had money to buy one."

"Never mind about money," says the man, "I'll give one free to the first of you who can solve this little puzzle: Pretend you are going around that circle in the same direction as the hands of a clock. Take away one balloon, then pass over two balloons and take away the third one, then pass over two more and take away the third again, and so on, round and round, until you have only two balloons left. Now, which balloon must you start with if the last two left are both to be blue ones?"

The pals think carefully. "I should start with the purple one," says Bill Badger. "No, the dark red one," says Rupert. "I should say it's the green one," murmurs Willie the mouse. "And *I* think it's the orange one," says Pong Ping.

(Does any one of the little people win a free balloon? Try it with eight pieces of paper.)

RUPERT'S PAPER LADDER PUZZLE

Rupert goes to Paper Town to buy some drawing-paper. While he is there he meets Snip and Trim, two quaint little paper people. They are looking very unhappy. "I wish you would help us, Rupert," says Trim. "We were playing with our kite when suddenly the wind blew it right into that tree. How can we get it down?" "You need a ladder," says Rupert at once. "I'll show you how to make one with a piece of my paper." Snip and Trim watch closely while Rupert folds the paper a certain way. "Now," he says, when it is ready, "with only *one straight cut* I can make you a splendid ladder!" Can you find out how Rupert makes his ladder, cutting a piece of folded paper once only? The secret, of course, is in the folding. The solution is given on the back page.

RUPERT

and the

DAFFODILS

Magic in fairyland showing how bad deeds always earn punishment.

One day the postman brings a surprise for Rupert's Mummy...

A present from Uncle Bruno! What a beautiful vase!

I know where I can find some daffodils...

It can't be!

But it is! A black daffodil!

Rupert's Daddy is just as astonished when he sees the flower...

Well, I never!

Haven't you heard of them then?

No...it's not even in my big book of plants.

Mr. Anteater...

Have you ever seen a black daffodil?

Never! And I hope this is the only one. They should be yellow!

Next day Rupert is working in the garden when...

Rupert! Come and see this!

Barbara!

You're never going to believe this!

What's this all about?

Black daffodils again!

What do you mean "again"? Have you seen them before?

17

Black daffodils! Like them, eh?

Who on earth are you?

.You're an imp, aren't you?

Silly question! Of course I am!

You know about those black flowers? don't you? Stop!

'Course I do! Catch me if you can!

Got you...

AAAGH!

Missed me! What a shame!

Now, covered in mud, Rupert is getting cross...

I'll wipe it off. Are you all right?

Yes. But he was too fast for me.

I know! We'll hide over there...

Then what?

Then we can see the whole park... look!

It's him again!

Right! You won't get away again!

Let me go! Let me go!

If you don't let me go you'll be sorry!

What a nasty little thing!

You're coming with us!

18

Who on earth is that you have there?

It's an imp. Is Daddy in?

What if I do?

So you're the one who changes the daffodils' colour!

Not very polite is he?

We'll lock him up while we decide what to do with him.

After lunch Rupert's Daddy goes to ask Mister Anteater's advice...

Taking the imp something to eat. He may be hungry!

What are you up to, Rupert?

Oh, dear! No one likes me!

I'm sure that's not true! I've brought you some food!

Now tell me why you...

No, it's better if I actually show you. Come on!

I'm not sure Daddy would like...

Come on! I'm sure he wouldn't mind!

Maybe not. But I'm holding on to you!

Oh, all right! But this is far enough!

They stop! The imp strikes the ground with his wand and...

A FLOWER! Amazing!

Now how would you like to try?

19

Rupert takes the wand but as he raises it he hits a branch by mistake...

Oh, what have I done?

You've made a daffodil tree it seems!

Come on! I've something else to show you!

Hey, wait!

Keep the wand. I've got another.

You first. I'll hold the trapdoor!

Yes, but...

HEY! Open this trapdoor.

Hee-hee! Give them my love, won't you!

Give who his love?

Gosh! A cave!

Next moment Rupert is surrounded by angry imps, all carrying spears...

An intruder!

Don't try anything!

I'm only here because an..

Be quiet, you!

Save your tale for our King, intruder!

Come on!

Your Majesty! We have a prisoner here!

"We caught this intruder in the cave, sire!"

Rupert is given a chance to explain. But it's plain the King does not believe him...

"An imp? Imps don't do such things!"

"Then please do take a look, sir."

"You had better be telling the truth, little bear!"

"Black daffodils, indeed!"

"He's right! Black daffodils! Who has dared to do this?"

Now the King has to let Rupert go...

"We are sorry, young bear. Be sure that wretched imp shall be taught a lesson!"

"Please don't be too hard, sir!"

"Rupert! Where on earth have you been?"

"It's a long story. Come on, I'll show you."

"Oh, look! They're yellow once more!"

"Let's see if we can catch that imp again!"

"Hello, squirrel! Seen any imps lately?"

"I should say so. Wanted to change my fur to blue! I just got away!"

"Follow me! I'll show you where he is!"

21

He's here... inside this tree!

There he is!

What was that I heard?

Got you!

Let's think of something naughty to do!

Well caught, Rupert!

OH, NO!

Not you again!

Here's your culprit, sir! Please don't be too hard on him!

He's very young. We'll remember that!

And so the King orders the naughty imp to give up his wand for a year...

You deserve a reward, little bear. Now watch!

Isn't that beautiful!

More than enough to fill Uncle Bruno's vase!

The King strikes the ground with his wand and at once there are hareballs everywhere Rupert dashes off to fetch his parents...

RUPERT AND THE PAINTING PUZZLE

"Isn't my uncle a good artist, Rupert?" says Podgy. "He has painted six pictures of me—and each one is a little bit different from the others." The pals are standing in Uncle Plumper's studio, and Rupert gazes for a while at the six portraits of Podgy which have been painted on a big canvas. "Yes, your uncle is very clever," says Rupert. "But I don't think you are right about all of them being different. I can see two pictures which are exactly the same." Podgy is very surprised, but when he looks again he discovers that Rupert is correct. Compare the portraits carefully and try to find the two which are exactly alike in every way. The answer is on the back page of the cover.

THE RIDDLE OF THE SKIES

Rupert is testing out another invention by Bingo. This time the Brainy Pup has produced a new kind of telescope, and he is now waiting to hear if the others can see what he says he saw in the sky.

Can you see what Bingo saw? No, well turn to the back page of the cover, and then follow the instructions.

MRS. BEAR'S WASH-DAY PUZZLE

A jolly crossword for you to solve. The answers are on the back page

CLUES ACROSS

1. On the clothes-line you can see . . .
4. This helps to get things clean.
7. A word that sounds like "two".
8. Where Mrs. Bear hangs out her washing.
13. A clothes-line is often made of . . .
14. When clothes are dry Mrs. Bear . . . them.
16. One of two small words found in "bean".
17. Second day of the week.
19. Mrs. Bear is walking on this in the picture.
20. A two-letter word which is in "soft".
21. The name of a sign used in arithmetic.
24. Worn by Algy.
26. Used to fasten washing on the line.
27. A word meaning "new"

CLUES DOWN

1. Needed for wash-day.
2. When washing clothes the water should be . . .
3. Small horse, but not a clothes horse!
5. First number.
6. Half of the word "door".
9. Mrs. Bear wears it to keep her frock clean.
10. Loud noises.
11. Overturn.
12. Rupert wears a yellow one.
15. To catch sight of.
16. You carry shopping in this.
18. This makes clothes grubby.
21. Set of two things.
22. Mrs. Bear hangs her washing on it.
23. Worn on the foot.
25. Rub-a-dub-dub, three men in a . . .

RUPERT'S NEW COLOURING PICTURE

Here is a new way of colouring. The big picture is ready for you to paint, and the four small ones are your colour guides. Start work on the big picture by putting in all the shades of red shown in the first small picture. Next add all the blue shades, followed by the tones of green and lastly the yellow. When you have filled in all four colours your big picture will be complete. You can have some extra fun if you work carefully and add the three other colours to each of the small pictures.

RUPERT

and the
FLYING
BOTTLE

How Podgy Porker nearly floated out of sight through being too greedy.

One day when Rupert and his Mummy are out for a walk they spot mushrooms in a field...

"Oo, Mummy, may I go and pick some, please?"

"Now, don't be too long. It's lunch in an hour."

"GOSH! Whatever is that?"

"A flying bottle! It can't be!"

"I'm going to find out..."

"OOPS!"
"I'm slipping!"

"PLONK!"

Then out from the bushes pops an old friend, the little servant...

"Hello, Rupert..."
"Do you always swim fully dressed?"
"Come on! Help me out!"

"You'll never guess what I've just seen! It was a..."
"Let me guess... a flying bottle, eh?"

"There! More of them! I've been sent to catch them!"

It's my boss the Professor's new invention. But let's get you dry!

Soon Rupert's clothes are drying in the Professor's tower home...

As soon as you're dry we'll go up and see my boss.

Flying bottles! I still don't understand. What's going on?

Professor! A friend here to see you!

Rupert, how nice of you to call!

Hello, sir!

Why are all those bottles flying about?

Just something I've invented — RISING LIQUID!

So anything filled with it rises? Wonderful!

I'd love to stay and help you. May I?

The Professor agrees and Rupert is sent out to catch flying bottles...

I shan't be long.

I'll round them up in no time.

Catching bottles like butterflies! What a game.

I've got the lot! How about that?

You've been a big help. Take this rising liquid home to play with!

Oo, thanks!

Suddenly Rupert remembers he has to be home in time for lunch and hurries away ...

What's that, Rupert? Lemonade? Let's have some.

No, Podgy. Not lemonade. Come with me and find out.

Rupert! Where have you been?

Just wait 'til you hear! First, may I borrow a saucepan?

Now, watch! Rupert the Magician! A few drops in the pan ...

Put the lid on. Now let it go, Daddy!

Let it go?

OOOOH! How did you do that?

Rupert tells them the whole story. Then after lunch Podgy and he go into the garden ...

I have a great idea, Rupert! If I take a sip of that stuff maybe I could fly!

No, don't! For all we know it might be poisonous!

Never!

The Professor wouldn't have let you have it if it was.

30

But Podgy is just stupid enough to try a sip of Rising Liquid...

What a silly thing to do!

Oh, dear...I do feel very odd!

Oops!

Gosh! I'm stuck! Come on, get me down!

I can't reach! I'll run and get help!

Edward Trunk! The very person. Come on, quick!

Take hold of my trunk. We'll soon have you down.

Hold him, Edward, 'til I tie this rope round him.

He's the oddest balloon I've ever seen. Now what?

Rupert decides to take Podgy to the Professor, but on the way...

Wait! Let's ask Dr. Lion's advice. It might save us a trip.

Fantastic! I've never heard of such a case in my life!

Can't you make him heavier? Iron pills maybe?

H'm, I've never come across Rising Liquid.

It's a mystery to me.

I can't help. You must find someone who knows about such things.

We'll just have to go and see the Professor after all.

It's blowing a gale up here!

Down here too. Hey, not so fast, Edward!

Gosh, what a wind!

Give me a hand, Edward!

HELP! What's happening?

The rope's snapped that's what!

*R*upert and Edward run to the Professor's tower...

Get the Professor! Something awful's happened!

Come with me!

Yes, yes, I can see him now. We'll soon collect him in my 'plane. Don't worry!

This is really my fault for not warning you when I gave you the Rising Liquid.

After a flying pig, are you? I've just seen him heading north-east!

Thanks!

HEY! HELP ME!

HELP!

Don't worry! We'll soon have you!

32

Got you!

Easy does it! I'll pull you aboard!

Calm down, Podgy. I have a mixture that will get you back to normal.

A little later Podgy is himself again...

You can let him go now.

He won't float away!

That's much better, being my heavy old self once more.

Don't any of you ever drink from strange bottles!

What will you do now, Podgy?

Go home for a jolly good meal! I can't be heavy enough!

33

RUPERT IN THE GNOMES' WORKSHOP

The Handyman Gnomes are building a wonderful engine for Rupert. But when he visits their workshop cave the Chief Gnome looks worried and says, "Oh, Rupert! We have mislaid some of the parts, and we can't finish your engine until we find them." "What a pity," says Rupert. He looks at the drawing of the complete engine and realizes which of the pieces are missing. "We must hunt high and low until we find them," he declares. "Let's search the cave." You can join the search too. Carefully compare the unfinished engine with the small blue drawing and you will soon see which are the four missing parts. They are hidden somewhere in the picture, and when you have found them you can help to complete Rupert's new toy. Using thin paper, trace the outline of each hidden part, colour it as it appears in the picture, and then cut out each shape and paste it neatly in its right place on the engine. If you do this there will be no need to cut your book.

RUPERT AND THE B's

"Come and have a game of cricket," says Bill Badger, as he wheels his cycle up to where his pal is sitting. "Right-o, but I must finish this chapter first," says Rupert. "I'll be just five minutes. In the meantime I'll set you a competition. Your name begins with a B. Look around and see if you can find 20 other things beginning with B."

Can you find the 20 things in five minutes? There are more than 20 in the picture.

Puzzle No. 1. The blue border contains pictures of many different things. Take a pencil and paper and write down those which begin with the letter "B". To give you a start, the picture nearest the top left-hand corner is BANANA. Now do your best to find the others.

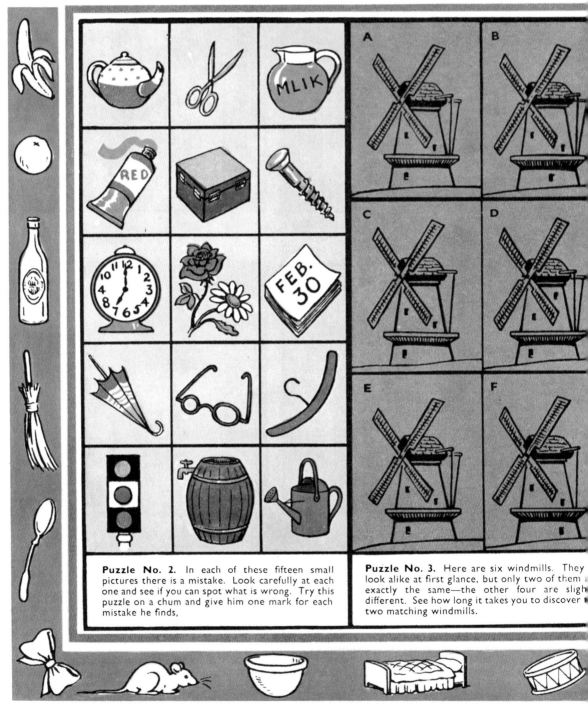

Puzzle No. 2. In each of these fifteen small pictures there is a mistake. Look carefully at each one and see if you can spot what is wrong. Try this puzzle on a chum and give him one mark for each mistake he finds,

Puzzle No. 3. Here are six windmills. They look alike at first glance, but only two of them exactly the same—the other four are slight different. See how long it takes you to discover two matching windmills.

OURITE PUZZLES

he answers are on the back page.

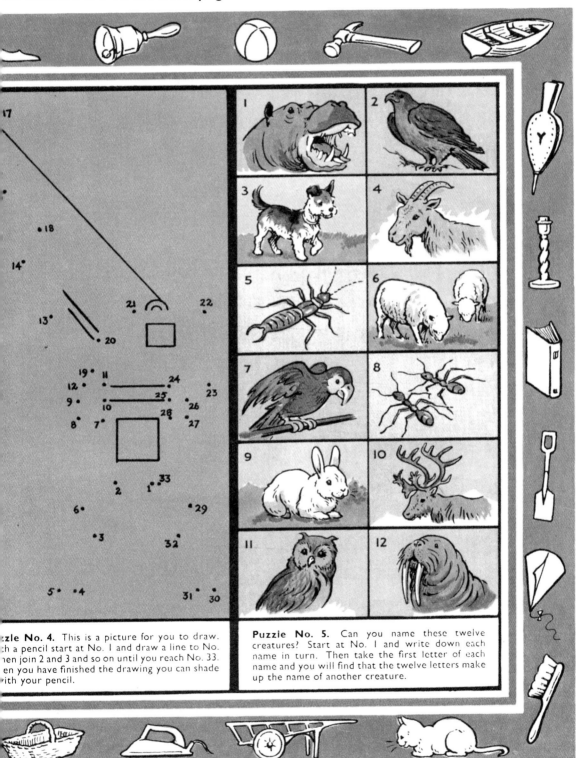

17

•18

14°

13°   21•   22

•20

19• 11
12•   24
9•   25   •23
10   •26
28
8• 7•   •27

•33
2• 1•

6•   •29

•3
32•

5• •4   31• •30

zle No. 4. This is a picture for you to draw.
h a pencil start at No. I and draw a line to No.
en join 2 and 3 and so on until you reach No. 33.
en you have finished the drawing you can shade
ith your pencil.

Puzzle No. 5. Can you name these twelve
creatures? Start at No. I and write down each
name in turn. Then take the first letter of each
name and you will find that the twelve letters make
up the name of another creature.

RUPERT IN THE MYSTERY CAVE

Rupert and his friend land from their small sailing boat and find a cave full of jewels. "Why, it's treasure of the old pirate days," says Rupert. "I know," says his friend, "but what are we going to do with it now we've found it?"

What can they do with four pirates watching them, and their frigate ready to sail? Look very carefully and see if you can find the pirates and their ship.

RUPERT
and the
RUBY RING

*How Rupert, by kind-
ness to an eel, is led
to treasure which brings
joy and happiness to two
lonely people.*

1 It's the time of year for tadpoles and Rupert thinks he'll catch a few...

See you later, Mummy!

Enjoy yourself but do be careful, dear!

Hello, hedgehog! What's amusing you?

Go and have a look! There's an eel acting very oddly!

What can it be playing at?

Hang on. Maybe I can catch it.

Got you!

Now, what's this all about?

Please help me...

There's something round my body. I can't get it off.

Tight round the eel's body is a valuable-looking ring...

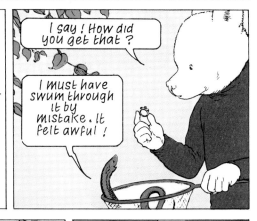

I say! How did you get that?

I must have swum through it by mistake. It felt awful!

That's a relief. Thanks, little bear!

Not at all!

HEY!

OOPS!

Hang on tight! I'll pull you out!

40

Thanks a lot! I'm Rupert Bear.

My name's Peter!

Been swimming, Rupert? Hee hee!

I'd better change before I catch cold!

My goodness! I did tell you to be careful!

After a hot bath Rupert tells his story...

It's a lovely ring! And it was round an eel, you say?

It has a coat of arms on it!

I'm sure it must be valuable!

A friend of mine knows about such things. I'll write to him!

Oh, please! May Rupert and I take the letter?

And so...

That must be the place your Daddy means.

Mr. Bear's friend is at home. And isn't he surprised...

?

Amazing! This ring was my father's!

It was stolen from our castle years ago!

There! Our coat of arms. Just as on the ring!

That's our castle. I can't afford to live there since so many of our things were stolen!

41

Tell you what; we'll find that eel again and ask it where it picked up the ring.

Let me know how you get on.

I saw it near here last, Peter!

That's it!

Remember me, eel?

Why, yes! What can I do for you?

Rupert tells the eel, and in turn learns what he wants to know...

A boat! Now that's handy!

Follow me!

Hours later...

I know this town! We'll soon be at the coast!

This is the place!

Thanks a lot, eel!

Right, we'll tie the boat to this and...

Ssh! There's someone coming!

Now, what are that pair doing here?

Look at that! An old chest!

Maybe they've smugglers or something...

Rupert, look! That coat of arms again!

 *The trunk is far too heavy to move so Peter and Rupert go for help...*

Where are we going, Rupert?

I'm not sure! Let's see where those stairs lead.

Sandy Bay! I've been here on holiday!

Let's hope the Punch and Judy show's still here with my chum Toby.

Oh, what a pity!

They must have moved on!

I remember you!

You know my pal Toby, don't you?

 *Rupert explains his problem and the man says he'll help...*

I say, what a climb!

It's a bit of a weight! Where do you want it?

As far from here as we can.

They certainly won't find it easily now!

Could you open it for us?

Look at that! The stolen treasure!

The three of them decide to take the treasure home by boat...

43

Hurry up, chaps! Those men may be back any time!

That's the lot!

It must be worth an awful lot!

Rupert thanks the performer for his help and then...

Let's leave it as heavy as we found it, eh?

They've just finished when the villains return...

Everything's prepared. Let's get the stuff out of here!

Once we've sold this lot we're rich for life!

Quickly, Rupert! Any moment now they'll find that trunkful of stones!

It's not here either. HEY! COME BACK YOU TWO!

Thanks! But I don't think we shall!

Hey, look! The river police!

The performer must have fetched them.

We'll take you youngsters home. Our mates are picking up those thieves.

The old man can't believe it! After all those years. His family treasure back...

Thank you so much, youngsters!

Believe me, there'll be a reward for this!

44